# I Am Thankful

# I Am Thankful

## A Thanksgiving Book for Kids

By Sheri Wall

Illustrated by Holly Clifton-Brown

ROCKRIDGE
PRESS

For general information on our other products and services or to obtain technical support, please contact our Customer Care Department within the United States at (866) 744-2665, or outside the United States at (510) 253-0500.

Rockridge Press publishes its books in a variety of electronic and print formats. Some content that appears in print may not be available in electronic books, and vice versa.

Interior and Cover Designer: Suzanne LaGasa
Art Producer: Karen Williams
Editor: Orli Zuravicky

Illustration © 2020 Holly Clifton-Brown. Author photo courtesy of © Erin Riddle.

ISBN: Print 978-1-64611-553-2 | eBook 978-1-64611-554-9

R0

*Dedicated to the spirit of gratitude*
*within each and every heart.*
*—SW*

The calendar says
November is here.
The leaves do a dance,
fall colors appear.

Family and friends,

with grins ear to ear,

will gather together–